Contents

Safety Notice
Please note that some activities require adult help and supervision.

Billy the Sheep in

Train Trouble

1 Billy the sheep was exploring the far end of his field. He had found a rather nice clump of juicy grass. He settled down and started to munch, munch, munch.

2 On the other side of the fence there was a railway line. It wasn't the sort with trains passing all the time. It was an old-fashioned line that was only used at weekends.

3 The railway line was used by people who liked to rebuild and drive old steam engines. It was popular with visitors who enjoyed having a ride in the rickety carriages.

4 When a steam train passed the lambs rushed to the fence and leapt about in a frisky sort of way. The passengers pointed and waved at the lambs and took their photograph.

5 Billy had always wanted to have a ride on a steam train. He often dreamt that he was an engine driver driving carriages full of lambs, and his field was full of people eating grass!

Text: Dave Wood   Illustrations: John Shackell

6 It started to get windy, so Billy moved to shelter behind a big tree. The lambs tried to huddle up to him out of the cold wind. They ended up climbing on top of each other.

7 Suddenly there was an extra strong gust of wind. With a lot of bleating, the pile of lambs fell into the field. As they bounced off the grass, there was a loud noise. C-R-E-A-K!

8 "Baa!" said Billy, which means, "Run!" in sheep language. The creaking noise got louder, then – CRASH! – the tree fell on to the fence. Clouds of earth and leaves flew into the air.

9 When the dust and leaves had settled and the animals that had lived in the tree had found new places to sit, Billy and the lambs looked at where the tree had landed.

10 The tree had fallen across the railway line! "Baa!" said a lamb. She pointed along the track. In the distance, behind a hill, there was a cloud of smoke. The train was coming!

11 Billy knew that by the time the train came round the corner and the driver saw the tree blocking the line, it would be too late for him to stop. The train would crash!

12 Billy is a clever sheep. He knows how steam trains work. He had watched them chug past his field for a long time. He thought hard, then gathered his friends around him.

13 Billy told the lambs what to do. They rushed off to the old barn. They went inside and bleated loudly. Soon a voice from high above them said, "Whooo!" It was Colin the owl.

14 The lambs told Colin what had happened. He quickly flew off to gather up some of his friends. Before long, he arrived at the fallen tree with another owl and two kestrels.

15 Each of the birds held a piece of Billy's woolly coat in their claws. They lifted him up into the air. They carried him to the pond and dunked him in it. Billy was soaking wet!

16 The birds flew towards the train still carrying Billy. "Baa!" called Billy, as they flew over the engine. The birds dropped him. Billy fell straight into the funnel of the engine!

17 The water dripped from Billy's fleecy coat. With a loud HISS, the water fell into the engine's boiler, and put the fire out. The engine started to slow down.

18 "What's going on?" said the driver. He wasn't used to seeing a large wet sheep being dropped into the funnel of his engine by a flock of birds! The train stopped near the tree.

19 The driver realised what had happened. This was a very clever wet sheep! He had stopped the train from crashing. "Hooray for Billy the sheep!" cried the passengers.

20 The train driver was pleased with Billy. He had a special station built by Billy's field. There was a small sheep-sized carriage, too, that Billy could ride in whenever he liked.

Body Games

Try playing these fun games at your Beaver Scout Meeting. The only equipment you need is your bodies!

Stork wrestling

Two players stand face to face. They each lift one leg by the ankle. They grip their free hands together as shown. On the count of three, each player tries to knock the other off balance. The first player to put a leg down or let go of the other's hand is the loser.

Shoulder push

Two players kneel, face to face. The players put their hands behind their backs. Using only shoulders, chest and neck, each player tries to knock the other off balance. The player left upright wins.

Text: Peter Barker   Illustrations: Phil Garner

Untangled

Eight or more players stand facing each other in a circle. All close their eyes. Players put out one arm and grab the first hand they find. Players then grasp their partner's other hand. With hands still linked, players open their eyes and try to untangle each pair from the group.

Sitting circle

At least ten people stand in a circle, all facing the same way. Players move closer to the person in front and when they hear the word "GO!" they all try to sit down. With care players should be able to sit on the knee of the person behind.

Life in the Seas

The waters of oceans and seas cover more than half the earth. They are home to many kinds of fish and animals.

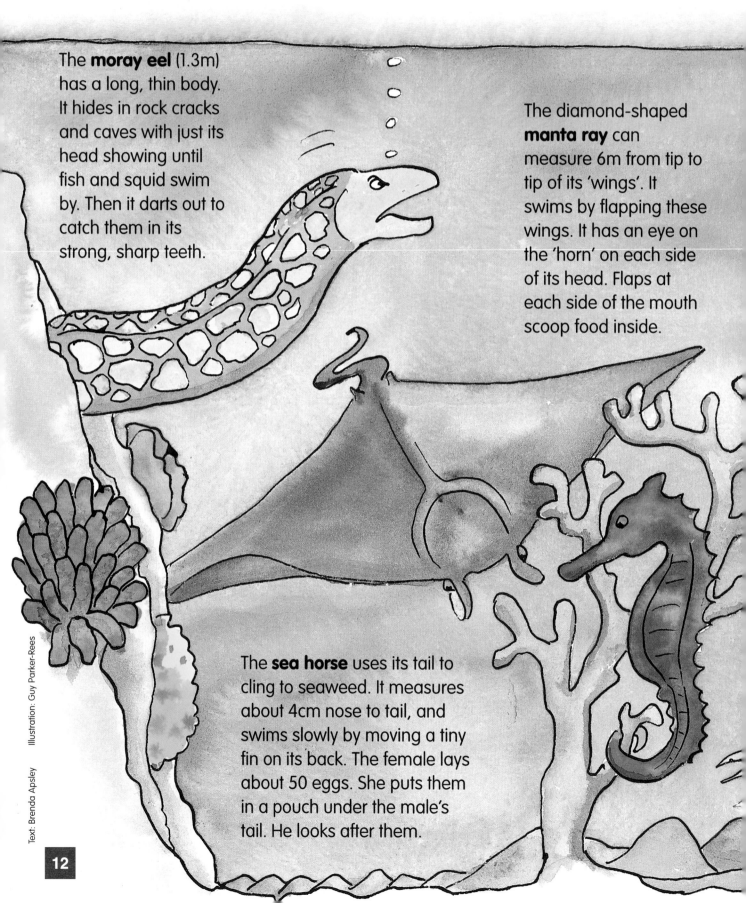

The **moray eel** (1.3m) has a long, thin body. It hides in rock cracks and caves with just its head showing until fish and squid swim by. Then it darts out to catch them in its strong, sharp teeth.

The diamond-shaped **manta ray** can measure 6m from tip to tip of its 'wings'. It swims by flapping these wings. It has an eye on the 'horn' on each side of its head. Flaps at each side of the mouth scoop food inside.

The **sea horse** uses its tail to cling to seaweed. It measures about 4cm nose to tail, and swims slowly by moving a tiny fin on its back. The female lays about 50 eggs. She puts them in a pouch under the male's tail. He looks after them.

Text: Brenda Apsley   Illustration: Guy Parker-Rees

The **flying fish** (30cm) beats its tail quickly to leap out of the water. It glides through the air on large fins which it uses like 'wings'. It usually 'flies' to escape enemies.

The **parrot fish** pulls weed from rocks to eat. It uses its special hard mouth like a beak, scraping off algae and coral to eat. Like the bird that shares its name, it is very brightly coloured.

The **porcupine fish** is covered in long, sharp spines. If it is in danger it swallows water so that its body swells into a fat ball. Its spines stick out, telling enemies, "Keep off!" It eats crabs and shellfish.

The **giant squid** can be 20m long. Strong muscles push it through the water very fast. It uses 8 shorter arms to steer itself and 2 longer arms called tentacles to catch prey. It squirts out ink as a smoky screen to protect it from its main enemy, the sperm whale.

Space Games and Puzzles

Answers on page 63.

Saturn's Rings

The rings around the planet Saturn are bands of clouds, made of millions of pieces of rock covered in ice. Can you steer the Voyager 1 probe through the maze of rings to Saturn's surface?

LIFT OFF

Beavers

1 2 3 4 5 6 7 8 9 10 11 12 13 14 15 16 17 18 19 20

Lift-off!

Play with a friend. You need a coin and a small counter each. Start at 20 at the base of the rocket. Take turns to flip the coin.

◆ If the coin lands HEADS up, move 1 space up the rocket.
◆ If the coin lands TAILS up, move up 2 spaces.

Who will be first to reach 3, 2, 1, then LIFT OFF?

To play on your own, count the number of flips you need to complete the game. Can you finish in fewer flips next time?

Text: Brenda Apsley   Illustrations: Mike Turner

14

Seeing Stars

Stars are shining balls of gas. We can see about 6,000 from Earth without a telescope. Stars are easiest to see on very dark nights from places where there are no street lights.

Play the star game with a friend. Take turns to draw pencil lines from one star to another. If your line makes a triangle, write the first letter of your name inside it and have another turn. When all the stars are joined, count the letters. The player with most letters is the winner.

Rub out and play again, or draw a game with even more stars on a sheet of paper.

Moon Landing

The moon is our nearest neighbour in space. There is no water on the moon so plants and animals cannot live there. The first spacecraft to take men to the moon was Apollo 11. On 21 July 1969 the American astronaut Neil

Armstrong became the first man to walk on the moon. He called his first step, "One small step for a man, one giant leap for mankind."

Two pieces of the moon landing jigsaw picture are missing. Which two pieces will fit? Draw them in and finish the picture.

Doodle and Scribble in...

The Jealous Little Alien

Many years ago, before you were born, a strange craft from outer space crash landed in Hill Wood near the little town of Lucas End. On board were two alien creatures, Doodle and Scribble. They liked the woods so much they decided to stay on Earth for a while. Since that day they have had many adventures. This is one of them...

One day, a Thursday actually, Doodle and Scribble were in the woods looking for worms to eat. They heard the sounds of children playing and decided to investigate. Safely hidden out of sight, they watched a group of children in grey sweatshirts and coloured scarves playing a game with a ball.

"They are young humans called Beaver Scouts," Doodle told Scribble. "They have

Text: Mike Brennon   Illustrations: Jo Turner

fun and make friends. That hut over there is where they meet." Scribble liked the sound of that. "Can I be a Beaver Scout?" he asked.

"No, Scribble," said Doodle. "It's impossible. We can't let the humans know we're here."

"It's not fair!" said Scribble. He felt jealous of the children. Like many jealous people, he decided to do something bad because he thought it would make him feel better.

During the next week Scribble collected eggs from birds' nests in the woods. He didn't tell Doodle, because he knew Doodle wouldn't approve.

The next Thursday the Beaver Scouts began to arrive at the hut for their meeting. What they found there upset them very much. All the windows were covered in messy broken eggs. The grass near the hut had been dug up and turned over, too. There was soil everywhere.

"Oh, dear," said Keema, the Beaver Scout Leader. "I think this is the work of vandals. I'm sorry, but I'm afraid we'll have to cancel this week's meeting while I go to the police station to report what has happened. We'll come back tomorrow and clear up the mess."

Doodle and Scribble were in the woods eating worm sandwiches.

"I wonder if we'll see the Beaver Scouts again," said Doodle.

"Not this week we won't!" said Scribble nastily.

Doodle looked towards the hut. He realised what had happened right away.

"Scribble! You spiteful little alien!" he said. "Did you make that mess?"

Scribble knew there was no point in telling lies. It always made things worse.

"If I can't have fun and make friends, then nobody can!" he said.

"Just because you can't have your own way doesn't mean you can ruin things for other people, Scribble," said Doodle. He explained what a bad thing jealousy is. Then he gave Scribble an idea of how he could put things right.

The next morning when Keema and the Beaver Scouts arrived to clean up, they saw an amazing sight. The windows of the hut were spotless. The soil had been cleared up and there were new flower beds around the hut, filled with flowers.

Of course, what they didn't know was that a small alien had spent the whole night scrubbing, cleaning and planting as his way of saying 'sorry'.

Doodle and Scribble watched, hidden in the trees.

"Well done, Scribble," said Doodle. "You can't be a Beaver Scout, but you can learn how to behave like one."

And Scribble smiled a happy, alien smile...

Sleep

We all need sleep. It is just as important to us as food, water and shelter.

Some people find it difficult to sleep. This is called **insomnia**. Things like worry and illness can make sleeping difficult. So can drinks like coffee and cola.

Sleep is when we rest. Our eyes close and our muscles relax. Our brains slow down.

We need sleep. People who do not get enough sleep can have headaches. They have trouble paying attention and can be bad tempered.

Different people need different amounts of sleep. Children need more sleep than adults. Most grown-ups sleep for between seven and eight hours each night.

There are many ways of getting to sleep. Exercise or reading before bedtime makes us tired and ready for sleep. A favourite way of getting to sleep is to imagine sheep jumping over a fence and counting them. The idea is that by the time you have counted lots of sheep you will be asleep!

Text: Mike Brennan   Illustrations: Mike Turner

The average human being spends one third of his or her life sleeping.

"THAT MEANS I'VE BEEN ASLEEP FOR..... 30 YEARS!"

Dreams are pictures or stories that appear in our minds while we sleep. We all dream every night, but sometimes we don't remember the dreams. A scary dream is called a nightmare. Nightmares are not nice, but they are harmless, so don't be afraid of them!

While we are asleep and dreaming our eyes sometimes move very quickly, even though our eyelids are closed. This is called REM – rapid eye movement.

Some animals sleep at night, but some sleep at any time of the day or night.

Some animals sleep for very long periods of time during the cold winter months. This sleep is called hibernation. Some animals get ready by eating lots of food which they store as fat in their bodies. Other animals collect food and store it to eat when they wake up during hibernation. Dormice, shrews, hedgehogs, bears and some bats hibernate.

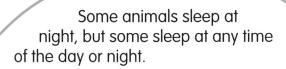

Bikes!

Do you have a bike? Let's find out more about them, and how to look after them.

Sometimes the simplest ideas are the most important. The wheel is what makes lots of machines work. Because they are smooth, with no corners, wheels spin. Wheels let bicycles roll along smoothly. They were first fitted to carts in about 3000BC.

A kind of bicycle was invented in France in about 1790. It was a small wooden horse with two wheels and a saddle. The rider pushed with his feet against the ground. Later the machine was improved so that the front wheel could be steered. Races took place in Paris, with riders travelling at up to 15km/h.

In England the machine was called a hobbyhorse. Cycling schools taught people how to ride. Riding was hard work. Some riders wore special shoes with iron soles to protect their feet.

Kirkpatrick Macmillan of Scotland made the first two-wheel cycle with pedals. It had wooden wheels with iron 'tyres' – but no brakes!

The bicycle is a simple machine. Powered transport like cars release poisons into the air. Cycling is friendly to our environment because the only power it uses is your energy. Cycling does not cause pollution.

About 500 years ago a famous Italian artist called Leonardo da Vinci drew a design for a machine with two wheels that a man could sit on and drive along.

Illustrations: Eric Rowe

Text: Brenda Apsley

Cycles called 'boneshakers' had pedals on the front wheel.

Some had solid rubber tyres and a padded saddle but they were still very heavy (about 30kg) to ride on rough roads.

The penny farthing was built in about 1870. It got its name from its big front wheel (like a penny coin) and its small back wheel (like a smaller farthing coin). In 1884 Thomas Stevens of America bicycled around the world on one. It took him two and a half years!

Two important changes were made to bicycles in the 1880s. The first was a back wheel driven by pedals and a chain. The second was inflated tyres that made riding more comfortable. These 'safety' bicycles with wheels of equal size are what modern bicycles are based on.

Here's how to get the best from your bike

* Make sure it is the right size. Sitting on the saddle, you should be able to touch the ground with one foot.
* Learn to ride SAFELY. Always wear a safety helmet. Do a cycling safety and skills course.
* Keep your bike clean. Wipe off mud, dust and grease. Dry your bike with a soft cloth if you have been riding in the rain. Keep it in a dry place.
* Always check your brakes and tyres before you ride.

A Fire Station

You don't often get the chance to visit a fire station – unless you're a Beaver Scout!

We have all seen fire engines racing past on their way to put out fires, with blue lights flashing and sirens screeching. Let's join a group of Beaver Scouts who visited a fire station in St Albans to see fire engines close up and to meet some fire fighters.

1 Fire engines carry all sorts of ▶ equipment. Different kinds of ladders help the fire fighters to reach high buildings. The Beaver Scouts looked at some ladders. They were even allowed to climb a few steps!

◀ **2** Water hoses connect up to the fire engine, and to special water pipes in the streets marked with yellow posts. William and Alex were shown how to hold a hose.

◀ **3** Fire fighters use a lot of special equipment. They wear special clothes to protect themselves from heat and smoke. They wear hard helmets to protect their heads. William tried on a helmet.

4 Alex, Josh, Daniel and James fired some water from a hose.

Text and photographs: Peter Barker

24

5 Josh and James tried on some helmets and special jackets.

6 The smoke made by fires is very dangerous. Fire fighters wear special air tanks and masks so that they can breathe in thick smoke. They are very heavy. Alex tried on a tank and a mask, even though he could not lift it!

7 Each fire fighter's clothing and equipment is neatly laid out in the back cab of a fire engine. It is always kept ready so that the fire fighters can change into it as they are travelling to a fire.The Beaver Scouts climbed into the back cab to take a look.

8 The front cab of the fire engine has a radio so that the fire fighters and the staff at the station can talk to each other. Daniel climbed into the driving seat. He was careful not to touch any of the buttons and switches!

9 The sides of the fire engine lift up. This is where hoses, ropes and other special equipment is stored. It was the perfect place for an end-of-visit photograph!

Snack Sticks

Food on sticks is fun to make – and even more fun to eat!

Kebabs are small pieces of meat and vegetables cooked on sticks. To make some mini kebabs at home you will need wooden kebab sticks (from supermarkets).

You can use little cocktail sticks for **very** mini kebabs! Always ask an adult to help you in the kitchen.

Sausage Sizzler

1 Cut a **hot dog sausage** into chunky slices.
2 Cut a **mushroom** into chunks.
3 Cut a **tomato** into chunks.

4 Thread a piece of sausage on to a stick. Push it to the end. Add a piece of mushroom, then a piece of tomato. Repeat until the stick is nearly full. Leave some stick empty so that you can hold each end.

Cheesy Yum Yum (serve cold)

1 Cut some **Cheddar cheese** into small chunks.
2 Open a tin of **pineapple chunks**.
3 Thread pieces of cheese and pineapple chunks on to a stick.

Ham and Cheese Sandwich (serve cold)

1 Cut a thick slice of **bread** into chunks.
2 Cut some tinned **ham** into chunks.
3 Cut some **Cheddar cheese** into chunks.
4 Thread chunks of bread, ham and cheese on to a stick.

Text: Emma Wood   Illustrations: Jeannette Slater

Marshmallow Delight

1 Cut an **apple** into chunks.
2 Thread the apple on to sticks. Put a **marshmallow** between each piece.

Toffee Apple Surprise

1 Cut an **apple** into chunks. Thread them on to a stick.
2 Put the stick under the cold water tap so the apple gets wet.
3 Roll the apple pieces in **brown sugar**.

Get Cooking!

Ask an adult to cook the snack sticks. Do not do this yourself.
Put the sticks under a hot grill. Turn them every now and then, until the food starts to sizzle.
The sticks can also be cooked in a microwave, for about one minute on full power. Leave to cool before eating.

A Planets Mobile

This easy-to-make planets mobile will look great hung from the ceiling in your bedroom!

The solar system is the name we give to the sun, planets, moons, asteroids and comets in space. Our sun is a massive star. Travelling around it are nine planets. Why not find out more about them, and make this planets mobile?

You will need

- compass
- ruler
- paper
- colouring pencils, crayons or felt-tip pens
- fine string or wool
- sticky tape
- wire coathanger

You also need a grown-up to help you!

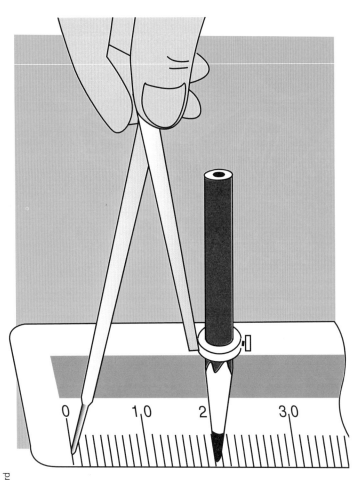

1 Use the compass to draw a circle for each planet. Put the compass point at zero on your ruler. Open the compass arm with the pencil until it is level with the measurement you need. These are listed in step 3. For example, move it to 20mm for Mercury, to draw a circle 40mm across.

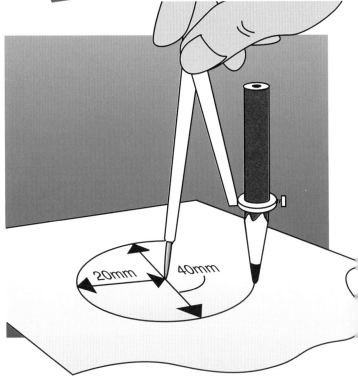

2 Hold the compass open at the measurement. Put the compass point on a piece of paper and turn the pencil arm around until you have drawn a circle.

Illustrations: Brian Folkard

Text: Ron Crabb

3 Draw the planets one by one. Cut out ▶ each circle, then colour both sides. Work from this list.

planet	compass setting	circle size	colour
(1) Mercury	20mm	40mm	brown
(2) Venus	30mm	60mm	red/brown
(3) Earth	30mm	60mm	blue/green
(4) Mars	20mm	40mm	red
(5) Jupiter	60mm	120mm	red/brown
(6) Saturn	60mm	120mm	brown/yellow
(7) Uranus	40mm	80mm	green
(8) Neptune	40mm	80mm	blue
(9) Pluto	20mm	40mm	brown

4 Cut nine ▶ pieces of string or wool between 12 and 20cm long, one for each planet.

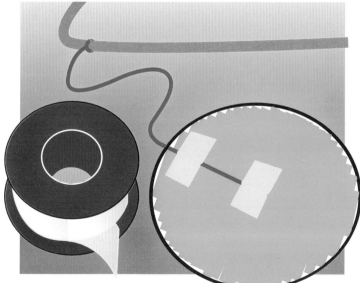

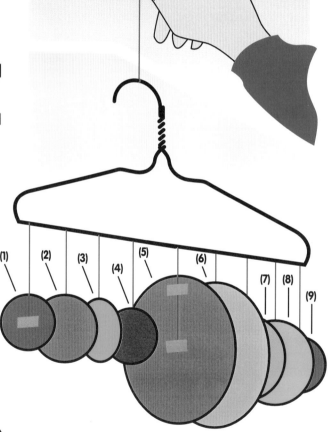

5 Using sticky tape, attach one end of each string to a planet. Join the other end to the bottom bar of the coat hanger. Fix all 9 planets in place in the same order as you made them. This is their order in the solar system. Mercury is nearest the sun. Pluto is furthest away.

6 Ask a grown-up to hang the mobile from your bedroom ceiling with a piece of string. The mobile gives you an idea of planet size, but they are not drawn to scale. In reality, Jupiter is more than 50 times the size of Pluto! Find out more about the planets in space books.

Beneath the Streets

What do you think is under your feet as you walk along? It's not just paving stones and soil. Let's find out what lies hidden beneath the streets.

Each section of this picture shows a level or layer beneath a city street.

- Just under the pavement in **level 1** are services that houses, shops and offices need. These include drains and telephone lines as well as electricity, gas and water supplies.
- The main sewers are in **level 2**. In big cities underground trains are here, too.
- Water supply tunnels are on the lowest level, **level 3**.

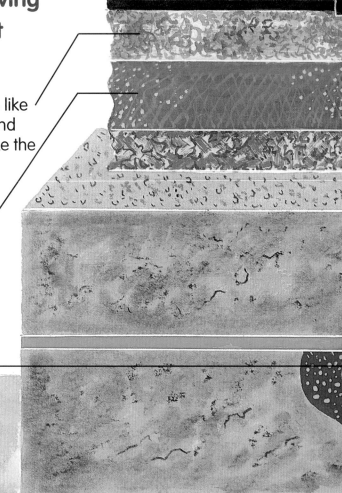

The **road surface** is crushed rock mixed with sand and bitumen.

A network of **sewers** carries waste to the large main sewer.

Drains take water from the street to the sewer.

Mixed rocks like limestone and granite make the **road base**.

Subsoil is the layer of soil below the top layer.

The main **sewer** takes waste away.

Large **tunnels** lined with concrete carry **water** to the city. Pumps take the water up to the surface.

Text: Alison Davis   Illustration: Eric Rowe

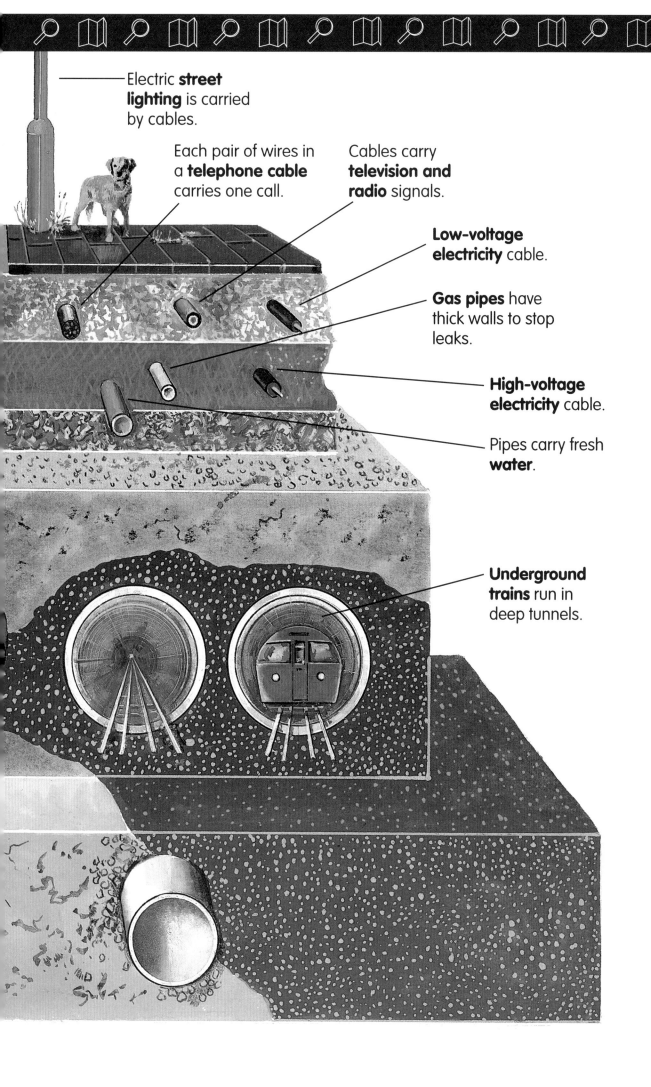

Electric **street lighting** is carried by cables.

Each pair of wires in a **telephone cable** carries one call.

Cables carry **television and radio** signals.

Low-voltage electricity cable.

Gas pipes have thick walls to stop leaks.

High-voltage electricity cable.

Pipes carry fresh **water**.

Underground trains run in deep tunnels.

level 1

level 2

level 3

Charlie and the Magic Camera

Charlie the Beaver Scout was going on a special day out at the seaside with his Beaver Colony.

When they were on the coach, Charlie took out his special camera. It was a lovely old Polaroid camera that always seemed to take nice pictures – even when it wasn't sunny! Charlie's Uncle Hamish had given him the camera. He said it was special – a special magic camera! Charlie wasn't sure about that, but the camera was still his favourite thing, just like old Uncle Hamish was his favourite uncle.

The Beaver Scouts had a lovely time at the seaside. They walked down the pier eating big ice cream cones and Charlie took a photograph of all his friends. It came out after a few minutes.

Then the Beavers went on rides at the fairground and Charlie took some more snaps of his friends as they whirled around on the roundabouts and went up on the big wheel.

After the fairground the Beavers went down on to the beach and had a picnic on the sand.

When they had all eaten their packed lunches some of the Beaver Scouts went for a paddle in the sea.

Charlie went to look in some rock pools. He hoped to get a photograph of a big crab, or even a starfish!

As he scrambled along the rocks, Charlie found himself on a very quiet part of the beach. There were caves in the cliffs and the rock pools looked very deep.

Suddenly Charlie heard a bark, then a splashing sound! Just ahead of him the rocks dropped steeply into the sea and Charlie could see a small dog splashing about in the water. Charlie looked around, but there was no one else to be seen. What could he do?

Illustrations: Mike Turner

Text: Sara Peach

To Charlie's surprise, a man dived into the sea from the rocks above him to rescue the dog. Charlie was amazed. He snapped a picture of the man as he pulled himself out of the sea on to the rocks.

"Here you are," said the man, and he handed the little dog to Charlie. Then he climbed back up the cliff.

"Wait..." said Charlie. But the man had gone.

Back on the beach, Charlie soon found the dog's owners. They had been looking

everywhere for him, and were calling his name. The dog shook wet drops of sea water all over Charlie, then he ran to his owners. They were very grateful to Charlie and listened carefully to what had happened. They looked very puzzled when Charlie told them about the man who had rescued their dog, and showed them his photograph. The dog's owners asked Mrs Green, the Beaver Scout Leader, if they could write when they got home to thank Charlie properly. Then they hurried off.

On the coach on the way home the Beaver Scouts looked at the pictures of their special day out. They enjoyed hearing about Charlie's adventure with the little

dog. When his story was finished Charlie was so tired that he fell asleep.

Later that week Uncle Hamish came to visit Charlie. As they were having tea, Mrs Green called. "I've had a letter from the owners of the little dog that fell into the sea," she said. "And look, they sent this story from an old newspaper. It's about a man who saved his own dog there many years ago. They knew him. He looks just like the man whose photograph you took."

Uncle Hamish looked at the newspaper picture and at Charlie's photograph. He smiled a special smile. "I told you it was a magic camera!" he whispered to Charlie with a big wink.

Charlie was amazed. What a story he had to tell at the next Colony meeting!

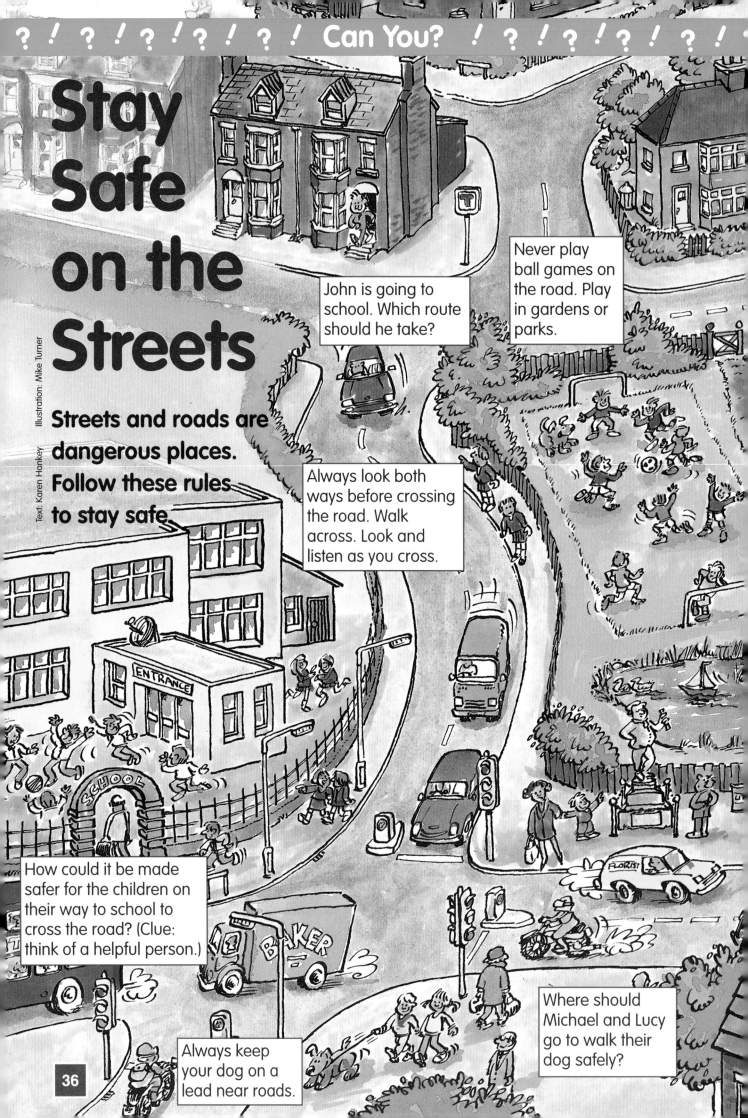

Stay Safe on the Streets

Streets and roads are dangerous places. Follow these rules to stay safe

Text: Karen Hankey   Illustration: Mike Turner

John is going to school. Which route should he take?

Never play ball games on the road. Play in gardens or parks.

Always look both ways before crossing the road. Walk across. Look and listen as you cross.

How could it be made safer for the children on their way to school to cross the road? (Clue: think of a helpful person.)

Always keep your dog on a lead near roads.

Where should Michael and Lucy go to walk their dog safely?

Magic!

Amaze your friends with the No Hole £5 Note Trick. It is easy to do but works like ... magic!

Get ready...

You will need
◆ a long envelope (the kind that opens at one end)
◆ a £5 note (a real one or one you have drawn)
◆ a pencil
◆ scissors

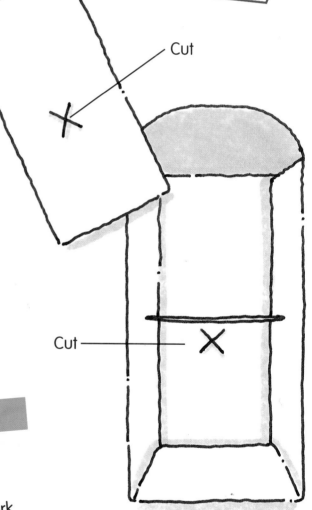

Cut

Cut

1 Cut a slit across the back of the envelope, as in the picture. Do not cut through the front of the envelope.

TRICK TIPS

❧ Practise the trick lots of times. Do it in front of a mirror.
❧ Make sure you can make the trick work well before doing it for an audience.
❧ Try to look and sound confident. DON'T giggle!
❧ NEVER tell anyone how the trick is done!

2 Below the slit, make two smaller cuts that cross. Make sure these cuts go through the back AND the front of the envelope.

Text: Peter Barker   Illustrations: Jeannette Slater

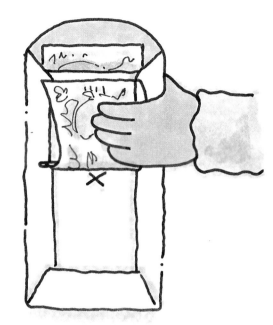

3 To do the trick, hold up the envelope with the slit facing you so that the audience cannot see it. Put the £5 note into the envelope. You must make sure that the note comes out through the long slit on the back. You should be able to see the bottom part of the note.

4 Without the audience seeing you, hold up the bottom half of the note as shown.

5 Pick up the pencil and push it right through the cross cuts. The audience will think the pencil has gone through the £5 note.

6 Quickly, pull the £5 note from inside the top of the envelope. Show it to the audience, who will be surprsied to see that there is no hole in it. Magic!

Colony Cocktails

These yummy cocktails are just the thing to cool your Colony down. They're easy to make and much more fun than orange or cola drinks. Chill out!

Bertie Beaver's Buck's Fizz

(serves 6)

600ml orange juice
45ml lemon juice
300ml bitter lemon drink
50g icing sugar
6 lemon slices

1 Mix the orange and lemon juice and the bitter lemon in a large jug.

2 Put the icing sugar in a sieve. Sift into the fruit juices. Mix well.

3 Chill in the fridge for half an hour.

4 Make a small cut to the middle of each lemon slice. 'Hang' a slice on the edge of each glass.

Text: Mike Brennan   Illustrations: Wendy Hesse

40

Colony Cooler

(serves 6)

900ml milk
500g fruit yogurt (your
    favourite flavour)
6 pink marshmallows

1 Pour the milk into a
large jug and add the
yogurt.

2 Whisk or stir until the
mixture is bubbly and frothy.

3 Pour into glasses.

4 Cut each marshmallow into four and
float the pieces on top of each drink.

Make your Colony Cocktails look extra
cool. Served them with fancy straws and
little paper umbrellas.

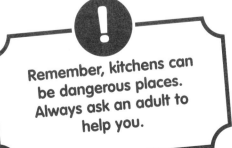

Remember, kitchens can
be dangerous places.
Always ask an adult to
help you.

Food Chains and Food Webs

In food chains different plants and animals are food for other plants and animals. Let's find out about them.

What is a food chain?

A chain is made of lots of pieces linked together. In a food chain each link is a plant or animal. Each one becomes food for the next one or ones in the chain.

Here is an example of a simple food chain.
Some grass (link 1) is eaten by a rabbit (link 2). The rabbit is eaten by a fox (link 3).

1   2   3

Green plants make their own food. They are the start of the food chain. They are **producers**.

Animals cannot make their own food. They must eat plants or other animals to live. They are **consumers**.

Here is an ocean food chain. Each animal is eaten by the animal next to it.

shellfish

squid

penguin   **seal**

killer whale

text: Mike Brennan   illustrations: Guy Parker-Rees

What is a food web?

Sometimes two or more food chains link together. This is a food web.

Here is a woodland food web. Each colour shows a different chain in the web.

All living things on Earth can be linked in one giant food web.

fox

shrew

vole

rabbit

insects

plants

sparrowhawk

sparrow

43

A Hammock Bird Feeder

Wild birds sometimes need help when food is hard to find. Make this bird feeder and have fun watching the birds use it.

You will need

- ✔ a grown-up to help you
- ✔ a long piece of rope
- ✔ thin wire netting with very small holes (from garden centres)
- ✔ plastic food bag ties
- ✔ wild bird food

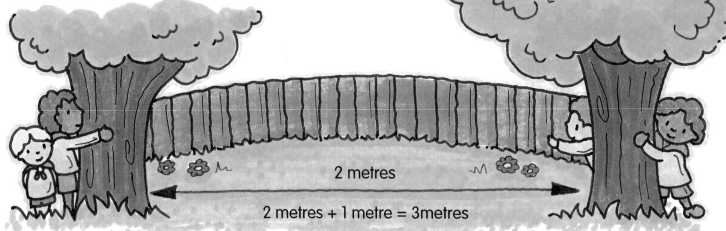

2 metres

2 metres + 1 metre = 3metres

1 The feeder will hang between two solid points like trees, the sides of a balcony, washing line posts or broom handles.

Measure the distance between the two points. Cut the piece of rope so that it measures this distance PLUS 1 metre.

2 Lay the piece of rope on the ground. Put a piece of wire netting under it.

Illustrations: Jeannette Slater

Text: Peter Barker

3 Roll the wire netting around the rope. Do not roll it too tightly.

4 Use plastic food bag ties to hold the wire netting in place. Use one at each end and two, three or four in the middle. Push them through the holes and twist.

5 Push wild bird food, nuts and scraps of bread into each end of the feeder.

6 Tie each end of the rope to an anchor point. Watch the fun as the guests arrive!

Tiger Alert!

The tiger is in danger of becoming extinct. Let's find out more about the largest member of the cat family.

The Indian tiger.

Mike Corley/WWF-UK

text: Stephen Nixey   Photographs: WWF-UK

Tiger Facts

A tiger can measure up to 2.7 metres. I metre of that total is tail! Its orange-yellow and black-brown stripes mean that it can move unseen through the light and shade of the jungle where it lives. This is called camouflage. No two tigers have the same pattern of stripes.

Tiger Food

The tiger is a carnivore, which means that it eats meat. It is a skilful hunter and catches deer, antelope, monkeys, fish and turtles using its sharp claws and large teeth. An adult tiger eats about 18 kilograms of food a day.

Thanks to their stripes, tigers can move around almost unseen.

David Lawson/WWF-UK

46

Tiger Homes

Most tigers live in the hot jungles and forests of Asia, especially in India, Indonesia and Malaysia. They do not like the heat, and rest at the hottest times of the day. They cool themselves in rivers. Siberian tigers live in snowy Russian forests. Some are striped. Others have thick white fur that blends in with the snow.

Tiger Families

Tiger cubs are born blind. They stay with their mother for about two years. They learn to hunt through play. The most important thing a cub learns is how to move silently, so that it can sneak up on its prey.

Like most tigers, these Siberian tigers enjoy cooling off in rivers.

David Lawson/WWF-UK

David Lawson/WWF-UK

Man is the tiger's greatest enemy.

Tigers in Danger

When Rudyard Kipling wrote about the tiger Shere Khan in his book 'The Jungle Book' 100 years ago, there were over 100,000 tigers in the world. Today there are about 5,000. Why?

The answer is man – the tiger's greatest enemy. In Asia tigers are still hunted for their skins and bones. Humans also destroy the places where tigers live as they set up new villages and clear land for farming. The sad fact is that unless something is done soon, tigers in the wild could be extinct in ten years time.

Tiger Conservation

People are trying to help tigers. In India 'Project Tiger' has been set up to help protect tigers from hunters. Many countries do not allow tiger skins and bones to be sold.

The WWF (World Wide Fund For Nature) is working hard to protect the tiger. They have set up safe tiger reserves, and work to stop poachers and train forest guards. They also try to get help for tigers from local people. They support projects that benefit people and tigers. Tourists can help by not buying tiger souvenirs and skins.

A Surprise Card

Surprise someone with this clever pop-up card.

You will need

* 2 sheets of coloured paper
* non-toxic craft glue
* scissors
* felt-tip pens

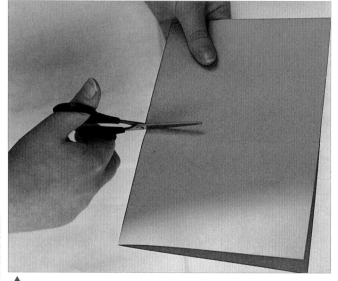

1 Fold one sheet of paper in half. Make a cut from the fold, near the middle.

2 Fold back the flaps to make two triangles. Tuck the flaps inside. ▶

Text: Karen Hankey   Photographs: David Garton

48

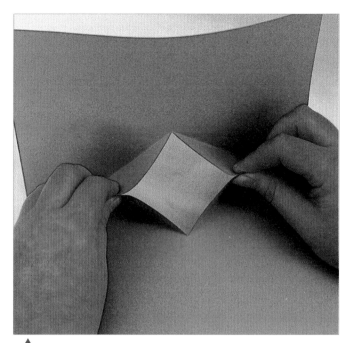

3 When you open the card, the flaps will look like a big mouth.

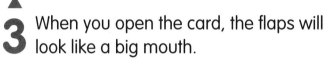

4 Spread glue over the back of the card. Don't get any on the flaps. Press on to the second sheet of paper. This will be the outside of the card. Keep it pressed closed until the glue is dry.

5 Draw and colour your card. Use bold, bright colours. This card is a frog, but you can make up a design of your own.

6 Why not add extra details like a long curly tongue and bulging button eyes? ▶

The Terrible Twins

1 It was a lovely, hot summer's day. The Beaver Colony were having a special fund-raising day. They were all helping to get things ready.

2 Luke and Jake were helping, too. They were identical twins. They looked the same. Everyone found it hard to tell them apart. This often meant trouble!

3 At last everything was ready. The Beavers were all given jobs to do. Luke and Jake were going to look after one of the stalls in the refreshments tent.

4 The twins were supposed to sell cups of tea and cans of cold drinks to visitors who came inside for a sit down. But every so often, Luke disappeared...

5 First Luke went off to have a go on the football game. He had to kick footballs into a five-a-side goal net. He got the top score and won a prize!

Story: Sara Peach   Illustrations: Jon Davis

6 Then Luke went off again. This time he had a go on the tombola stall. Most of his tickets were winners, and he came back with an armful of prizes.

7 The next time Luke went off, he saw a lady doing face painting. He had his face painted like a clown's. He looked very funny with his big red nose.

8 Luke saw the coconut shy on his next walk around the stalls. He threw three balls and each one knocked off a coconut. Luke won three prizes!

9 When Luke got back this time, Jake was mad. He'd had to work extra hard on his own on the stall. "It's my turn to have some fun now!" he said, and stomped off.

10 Jake wanted his face painting. "Go away, you naughty boy!" said the lady. "You've had your turn already. And you've rubbed off all the paint I put on so carefully!"

11 Jake decided to try the football game instead. "Go away!" said the boys in charge. "You've already won the top prize." Jake tried to explain, but they wouldn't listen.

12 The same thing happened at the tombola stall and the coconut shy. Jake was very fed up. Then he saw something he could have a go at. But he needed Luke...

13 Back in the refreshment tent Luke was very busy. Jake whispered his plan. The naughty twins crept out of the tent. They left behind a long queue of customers!

14 "Roll up! Roll up! The three-legged race is about to start!" said a voice over the loudspeaker. The twins won the race easily and Jake went up to collect first prize.

15 The next race was a wheelbarrow race. Guess who won? Yes, the terrible twins. Jake collected another prize. He was catching up with Luke now!

16 The twins entered the fancy dress contest. Jake rubbed some of Luke's face paint on to his face. They found clown costumes in the Scout Hut. They won first prize!

17 But Brown Beaver was waiting for them at the side of the stage. "There you are!" she said. "Come with me!" She marched the twins back to the refreshments tent.

18 There was chaos in the tent. A long line of thirsty people were waiting for drinks. And near the sink there was a mountain of washing up waiting to be done.

19 "Right, you terrible twins," said Brown Beaver. "I've got a very special job for you." Luke and Jack had a good idea what the special job was. Can you guess?

20 Yes, Brown Beaver wanted them to do the mountain of washing up. Jake had to wash and Luke had to dry. Who knows? The terrible twins could still be doing it!

Heathrow Airport

Beaver Scouts Andrew, Jonathan and Adam visited London's Heathrow Airport. Let's go with them!

▲1 At the Visitors Centre the boys were each given a clipboard, a pencil – and some questions to answer. If they answered most of them they would get a metal badge.

Have you ever been on an aeroplane? If you haven't, the next best thing is to visit an airport, where you can go with an adult to watch planes land and take off. Three Beaver Scouts from the 7th Windsor (Old Windsor) Colony asked their Leaders if they could visit Heathrow Airport's brand new Visitors Centre. They all had a really exciting time!

▲2 The airport opened in 1946. The Beaver Scouts looked at some of the clothes and things pilots used many years ago. "They wore goggles and leather hats," said Adam. "The hats had special flaps to keep their ears warm."

◀3 Part of the centre looks like a real airport check-in area. The Beavers went through the metal detector and set off the alarm bells with the metal on their clipboards!

4 They weighed Andrew on the luggage scales. The scales are used to make sure people's bags aren't too heavy for the planes to carry safely. ▶

Text and photographs: Dave and Emma Wood

▲ **5** The boys did some brass rubbings. They laid paper over a picture of an aeroplane carved in a sheet of brass. "If you rub over the picture with a crayon," said Jonathan, "you can see the aeroplane."

▲ **6** This picture of the airport was taken from the sky. "It's about four times bigger than the size of the village you live in," Little Hand told the boys. "And nearly 50 million people pass through each year."

◀ **7** "Look at these old pictures," said Jonathan. "In the old days, when the airport first opened, there were only big tents, not buildings!"

8 Andrew studied a sheet which told him how many different airlines fly to and from Heathrow Airport. ▶

9 The boys looked at real planes to try to spot the coloured tail fins which say which airline owns them, like these:

Air Canada   Air France   Swissair   Air 2000   Cyprus Airways

Cartoon Faces

Drawing faces that look real is tricky and needs lots of practice. Drawing cartoon faces is easier, and much more fun! Here's how.

Start by deciding on the shape of the head. Most heads are oval but some are short and round. Other heads are long and thin – and some are egg shaped!

1 Draw the head shape you have chosen. Use a light pencil like an H.

2 Draw eyes. They go just above the middle of the head.

3 Draw a nose. It begins at the eyes and ends just above the mouth. Draw the mouth in the middle of the bottom half of the head.

✎ Use a rubber eraser to rub out any part of the face you are not happy with. Draw it again.

✎ When you are happy with your drawing, go over the pencil lines with a felt-tip pen.

✎ Practise this way of drawing cartoon faces until you are good at it. Then try making new faces by changing the position of eyes, nose and other features.

✎ Make different looks or expressions by changing the shape of features.

4 Don't forget ears! Make them large, small, sticky-out – it's up to you.

5 Draw eyebrows. Their shape can make a face look very different. Add eyelashes, too.

✎ Try drawing different features to make:

a happy face   **a sad face**   **an angry face**

6 Last of all, draw some hair, long or short, curly or straight.

Text: Mike Brennan   Illustrations: Jeannette Slater

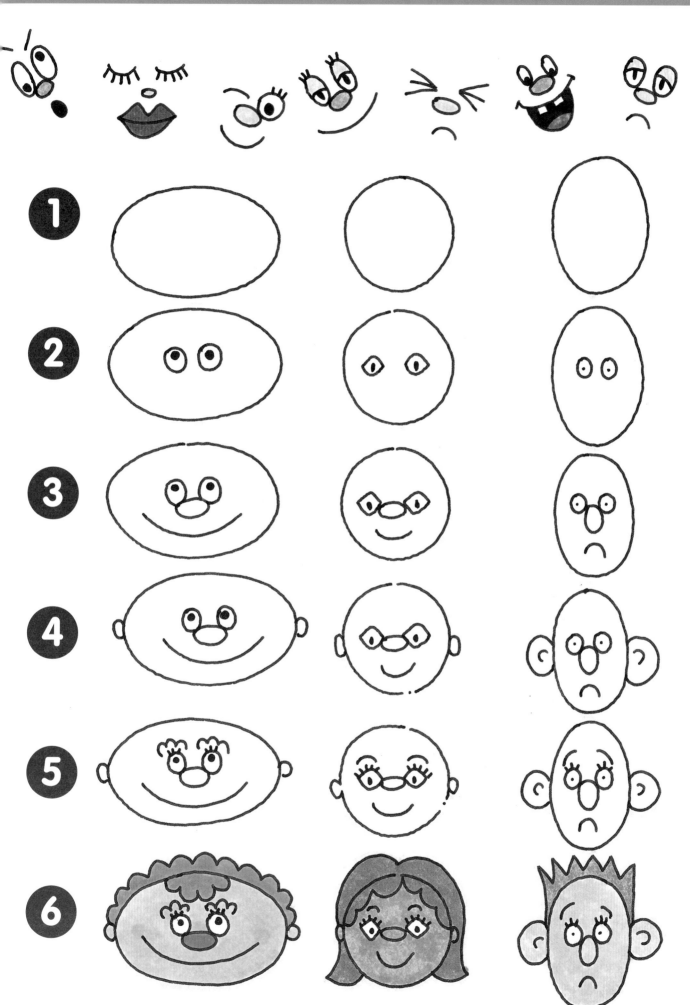

Animal Senses

Animals, like humans, use their senses of sight, hearing, smell, touch and taste to make contact with each other and find out what is happening around them.

Five senses

Most animals use a mixture of the five senses, not just one. An animal's senses match its needs. Often its strongest sense is the one that is most useful to it. Good eyesight is useful for hunters, but no use to animals that live in darkness.

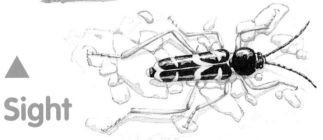

▲

Sight

Animals use sight for attack. When they are hunting, big cats like tigers creep up on their prey, always watching. Birds of prey have very good eyesight. The golden eagle can see a rabbit more than 1 kilometre away. Animals use sight for defence, too. Zebras have large round eyes and can see danger in front, at the side and behind.

Animals use colours as visual messages. These messages do not always tell the truth. The wasp beetle looks like a wasp. It is harmless, but its black and yellow stripes are a warning to other animals. The warning says: Do not attack. I am dangerous!

Sound and hearing

Sound is used by hunters. Big cats have good hearing. They use their ears to listen to movements that tell them prey is near. Good hearing is useful for animals that are hunted, too. Rabbits have very good hearing. They can turn their long ears to find where a sound is coming from.

Bats use their ears to help find their way in the dark, and to find food. As they fly they make high pitched squeaks that are too high for us to hear. These sounds bounce off objects like trees and flies. Bats know where objects are by the time it takes for the echo of the sound to return to them.

▼

Illustrations: David Webb

Text: Alison Davis

Smell ▶

Many animals hunt by smell. A dog's nose lets it 'see' the world as a pattern of scents and smells. A dog's sense of smell may be as much as one million times better than a human's!

Dogs and cats have special glands in their skin that make a smell they leave behind to mark their territory. When other animals smell it, it has a message for them: Keep away! This is my patch!

◀ Touch

We feel things best with our fingertips. Animal whiskers are very useful in the dark. Cats use them to find things they cannot see.

Moles live in the dark. Their long, sensitive whiskers help them feel their way around.

Taste ▶

Animals use taste in a similar way to smell. A tiger licks her young cubs to mark them as hers. Other tigers can 'read' the smell like a label.

Snakes taste smells by sticking out their tongue. Smells help them follow prey or keep away from danger. Flies taste food through their feet!

Colouring Competition

Beaver Scouts like to have fun.
Beaver Scouts enjoy a challenge.
Why not do both, and enter our Crayola® Colouring Competition?
You could win some great prizes for you and your Colony!

Create a little colour...with Crayola®

When it comes to colour, Crayola® 'know-how' brings you hands-on creative fun. So get creative and design and colour an emblem for your Colony. Talk to your Beaver Scout Leader about ideas. Perhaps you could draw something that is important to your Colony, or to your area?

Simple, colourful designs will work best, because the winning design will be made into special pin badges for you and your Colony to wear! You'll also win a bumper pack of Crayola® prizes, enough colouring pens and pencils, stampers and creative activities to keep any young artist busy!

And that's not all – we'll also include a selection of Crayola® goodies to share amongst your whole Colony.

Two runners-up prizewinners will also receive a selection of Crayola® goodies for their Colonies.

Write your name and address on the back of your entry. Send it, attached to the entry form, to the address on page 61, to arrive no later than 30th January 1998. The winners will be chosen after the closing date. You can photocopy the form if you don't want to cut the annual page.

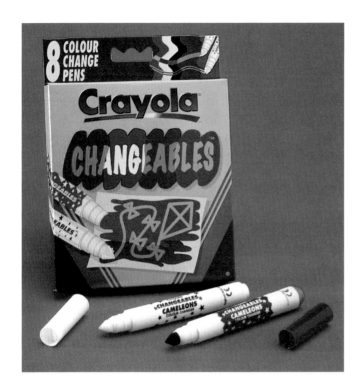

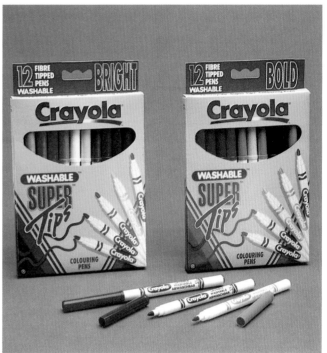

1998 BEAVER SCOUT ANNUAL COMPETITION ENTRY FORM

Name . . . .

Age and date of birth . . . .

Address . . . .

. . . .

Post code . . . .

Name of your Beaver Scout Colony . . . .

Address . . . .

. . . .

Post code . . . .

Send your entry to:
Crayola® Colouring Competition
1998 Beaver Scout Annual
The Scout Association
Baden-Powell House
Queen's Gate
London
SW7 5JS

Rules and conditions:
1. Entrants must be full members of The Scout Association's Beaver Scout Section at the time of entering the competition.
2. Entrants must be under the age of 8 years on 31st December 1997.
3. Prizewinners will be notified by post.
4. While every effort will be made to provide the winners with the prizes described, The Scout Association, World International and Crayola reserve the right to substitute alternative prizes of equal value.
5. No entries can be returned.
6. The judge's decision is final and no correspondence can be entered into.

And the Winner Is...

Max Reynolds of Dover, Kent. Congratulations!

Max's bike design was chosen as the winning entry in the 1997 Beaver Scout Annual 'Win a Bike' competition. Max is now the proud owner of a Raleigh Bronx Action Bike.

There were hundreds and hundreds of great entries, and a special thank you must go to all the Beaver Scouts who entered. It looks like there are lots of budding designers out there in the Beaver Scout Section! The quality of entries was very high, and this meant that judging the competition was not easy. However, in the end the judging panel, made up of staff at SCOUTING Magazine and The Scout Association's Publications Section, all agreed that Max's hamster-powered bike should be the winner.

Here is Max's
prize-winning design:

Once again, congratulations, Max, and many thanks from the judges to all of you who entered the competition.

If you fancy yourself as a designer, check out page 60 for this year's competition. Who knows, YOU may be the winner.

62